Word Bank
Expanding Y...

The better you are at ... successful you are likel... vocabulary is an impor... communicating skills, a... ...want your speech and writing to be clear, assured and persuasive you should be adding to it regularly. With a deceptively simple technique, *Word Bank* will effortlessly help you add hundreds of useful, apposite and elegant words to your everyday vocabulary.

The **One Hour Wordpower** *series*

WORD BANK
Expanding Your Vocabulary
WORD CHECK
Using Words Correctly
GOOD GRAMMAR IN ONE HOUR
THE NAME BOOK
THE SECRETS OF SPEED READING
GUIDE TO WORDPLAY AND WORD GAMES
CRISP CLEAR WRITING IN ONE HOUR
SPELL CHECK
1000 Most Misspelled Words

One Hour Wordpower

Word Bank

*Expanding
Your Vocabulary*

GRAHAM KING

Mandarin
in association with
The Sunday Times

A Mandarin Paperback
WORD BANK

First published in Great Britain 1993
by Mandarin Paperbacks
an imprint of Reed Consumer Books Ltd
Michelin House, 81 Fulham Road, London SW3 6RB
and Auckland, Melbourne, Singapore and Toronto

A CIP catalogue record for this title
is available from the British Library
ISBN 0 7493 1519 9

Printed and bound in Great Britain
by Cox & Wyman Ltd, Reading, Berks

Introduction

THE GREATER THE CHOICE, THE CLEARER THE VOICE

Here is art critic William Feaver describing an exhibition of paintings by Allen Jones:

> Allen Jones gives recitals of body-language (the jut of the silken bottom, the parting of the lips) and colour code (1,000-watt yellows, ice-maiden blue), tracing erotic lines that slither down the thigh and die away in drips and stains.

That verbal communication must surely be as vivid and exhilarating as the paintings it describes. In it, Feaver has obviously had at his elbow a formidable palette of words, none of them, incidentally, quaint or outlandish, but words ready to jump at his command to create a clear word-picture, yet also convey stimulating overtones of high excitement.

That is what communication, spoken or written, is about – clarity and colour: clarity to get your thoughts across unambiguously, and colour to attract attention and to 'sell' your message.

To help you achieve this you have all the advantages of the English language, which many regard as England's supreme gift to the world. Some 360 million people use its great lexicon of over 450,000 words, and a further 1.1 billion regard it as a second, official or dialect language. Only Chinese is used by more people, but as it is rumoured that more Chinese are currently learning English than the population of the United States, even that language may soon be eclipsed in global popularity.

As a very rough rule of thumb, the more words you

have available in your word bank, the more effectively you will be able to communicate. Shakespeare, who was no slouch when it came to communicating, possessed a vocabulary variously estimated at between precisely 17,677 words and approximately 30,000 words. At the other end of the scale, research on telephone calls in the US has revealed that 96% of all conversations were conducted with a vocabulary of only 737 words. In the middle, it is thought that an intelligent and reasonably well-read person in Britain has a word bank of between 7,000–15,000 words.

A 15,000-word vocabulary has many advantages over one of 7,000 words. If the essence of communicating is to convey what we mean with absolute clarity, then it is better to use words that express our thoughts precisely than words which merely approximate what we mean. In other words, the greater the choice, the clearer the voice. Inevitably, this calls for a vocabulary that recognises the differences between, for example, **flaunt** and **flout**, **parameter** and **perimeter**, **rebut** and **refute**, **saccharin** and **saccharine**, **turbid** and **turgid**, and so on.

Clarity, however, can go for naught if our efforts to communicate are flat and boring; nobody will want to listen to us. That's why we need even more words to colour our communicating, to make it flow, to sing, to captivate, to seduce, to sting. And there will also be times when the *mot juste (qv)* will not be found in our own language; so any serviceable vocabulary will include a selection of foreign words and phrases.

Word Bank is neither a dictionary nor a list of unusual and bizarre words, but a selection of words most people find useful, even essential, in their speech and writing. Many of them you will undoubtedly know; some of them you may think you know; while the balance will be new to you. Each entry is treated as a little puzzle or quiz, not to test your word power or IQ, but to help you commit the word, its spelling and meaning, to your memory.

Each time you do this, you are depositing a fresh word in your own word bank to be withdrawn when you need it. If you learn to use three new words a day, your vocabulary will have grown by 1,000 words at the end of a year. And the English language will be a little less like Flaubert's cracked kettle, 'upon which we beat out tunes for bears to dance to, while all the time we yearn to move the stars to pity'.

Acknowledgements

The definitions in *Word Bank* are necessarily
brief, so a good dictionary will prove to be a
helpful companion to this little book.

The following works provided the definitive
sources for meanings and usage in *Word Bank*:

*The Oxford English Dictionary, Cassell's English
Dictionary, Webster's New Twentieth Century
Dictionary, Collins English Dictionary, Funk &
Wagnalls Standard College Dictionary, The
Encyclopaedia Britannica, Fontana Dictionary of
Modern Thought.* Also *Fowler's Modern English
Usage,* Eric Partridge's *Usage and Abusage, The
Facts on File Encyclopedia of Word and Phrase
Origins, Chambers Science and Technology
Dictionary,* Robert Claiborne's *The Life and
Times of the English Language* and *The
Cambridge Encyclopedia of Language*
by David Crystal.

The publishers would like to thank
Collins English Dictionaries for permission
to reproduce the extract on page 15.

Word Bank

One of the best ways to expand your vocabulary is to pause when you see a word, the meaning of which you don't know or aren't too sure about, and look it up in a dictionary. Often, however, you spot the word that puzzles you on the train or tube or away from home, and by the time you get anywhere near a dictionary you've forgotten all about it. That's why it's a good idea to build up your knowledge of words in advance.

Word Bank will help you do this with a selective list of words of the kind that insinuate themselves into our everyday conversation and reading. Only minimum effort is required to choose or guess the correct meanings of the words and to fix them in your mind; but it's worth making the extra effort to look them up in a good dictionary for the complete and detailed definition or, in many cases, definitions.

A

Choose the correct meaning.

(Answers page 88)

abstruse	argumentative; hard to understand; scientific
accretion	increase by external growth; the components of concrete; the residue left by high tides
Achilles' heel	athlete's complaint; fashionable shoes by a Greek designer; vulnerable spot
acolyte	an attendant; oil lamp; rare mineral
acrimony	unclaimed treasure; bitterness; wild herb
actuary	hospital helper; insurance expert; part of a library where religious books are kept
acumen	pepper-like substance; penetrating insight; the ability to tolerate giddy heights
affidavit	a written statement made on oath; a solicitor's instruction; a judge's direction to a jury
aficionado	the sword thrust that kills in a bullfight; a keen fan or follower; a large wine barrel
agnostic	a religious hermit; a condition of the throat; a person who denies knowledge of God

agronomy	study of grasses; study of river pollution; study of soil
akimbo	hands on hips with elbows pointing away; legs wide apart; sitting with legs crossed
alfresco	famous New York salad; fizzy Italian wine; in the open air
alter ego	one's other self; slow opera movement; the membrane that encloses the yolk in an egg
amalgam	a compound of different metals; ash left from burnt ivory; fool's gold
amanuensis	a nurse specialising in tuberculosis care; a secretary; sewing machine mechanism
ambidextrous	ability to juggle with hands and feet; ability to jump long distances; ability to use both hands with equal facility
ambivalent	not complete; indecisive; unable to walk
amortise	to reduce or pay off a debt; to fix two pieces of wood together without nails or screws; to die leaving two or more wills
anachronism	type of lobster; collecting old clocks; a person or event misplaced in time
analogous	capable of being analysed; process for water-proofing shoes; similar in some respects
anathema	something hated; a love–hate relationship; a diagnostic technique for lung disease
angst	unfounded anger; mental instability; anxiety
annul	cancel; harden metal; every other year
animus	hostility; hairy; a spooky mist or fog
anosmia	inability to recognise the colour blue; inability to perspire; inability to smell
antipathy	hatred; aversion; fear

antonym	a word that makes sense when spelt backwards; a word of opposite meaning; a three-letter word
aperient	slow-working medicine; laxative; eye lotion
aphorism	a grammatical mistake; an embarrassing remark; a short, pithy saying
apiarian	relating to monkeys; animal rights; relating to bees
aplomb	poise and assurance; reckless abandonment; explosive anger
apocalyptic	prophesying ultimate destruction for all; semi-paralysed; denying religious freedom
apogee	edge of a plateau; tip of an iceberg; climax
apposite	directly behind; inappropriate; appropriate
apostasy	embracing several religions at once; renouncing one's religion or principles; returning to the Roman Catholic religion
appurtenance	an accessory; a boil on the neck; self-mockery
aquiline	green; smooth-surfaced; eagle-like
arachnid	spiny anteater; land crab; spider family
arbitrage	buying and selling securities on different markets to profit from differing rates of exchange; profiting from insider dealing; buying distressed futures of metals and commodities
arcane	rare and expensive; mysterious and secret; sweet and syrupy
argot	semi-precious stone; type of tobacco leaf; slang

How to use a dictionary

First, make sure you have a practical and up-to-date dictionary that you feel comfortable with. The 20-volume *Oxford English Dictionary 2* at £1,500 may be the ultimate in word reference books, but only a specialist would need it; at the other end of the scale there are mini and pocket-size dictionaries that can be worse than useless. Occupying the middle ground is a vast range of excellent dictionaries which in paperback can cost less than £5. Every bookstore and many large newsagents stock a selection (Oxford, Collins, Cassell's, Longmans, to name a few) so there is no excuse not to own this essential tool to help you expand your vocabulary.

A dictionary *defines* words; it does not usually explain how to use them. It describes, not prescribes. For guidance on how to use words there are books on English usage; for helping you find the word you want there are synonym dictionaries and the thesaurus.

An entry in a good dictionary offers quite a lot of compressed information. Let us analyse a typical entry (for the word *read*) in a typical dictionary (*Collins Paperback English Dictionary*, £4.99).

1. Main or Entry word, usually in bold type
2. Pronunciation, according to the International Phonetic Alphabet
3. Grammatical designation, in this case a verb
4. Participle forms of the main word
5. The first of fourteen different or differing meanings and usages of the word, often with examples

1.   **2.**   **3.**   **4.**   **5.**

read (riːd) *vb.* **reading, read** (rɛd). **1.** to understand (something written or printed) by looking at and interpreting the written or printed characters. **2.** (often foll. by *out*) to speak aloud (something written or printed). **3.** to interpret the significance or meaning of: *to read a map.* **4.** to interpret (signs, characters, etc.) other than by visual means: *to read Braille.* **5.** to have sufficient knowledge of (a language) to understand the written word. **6.** to make out the true nature or mood of: *she could read his thoughts.* **7.** to interpret in a specified way: *it can be read as satire.* **8.** to have a certain wording: *the sentence reads as follows.* **9.** to undertake a course of study in (a subject): *to read history.* **10.** to gain knowledge by reading: *he read about the war; a well-read young woman.* **11.** to register or show: *the meter reads 100.* **12.** to put into a specified condition by reading: *I read my son to sleep.* **13.** to hear and understand, esp. when using a two-way radio: *we are reading you loud and clear.* **14.** *Computers.* to obtain (data) from a storage device, such as magnetic tape. ~*n.* **15.** matter suitable for reading: *this book is a very good read.* **16.** a spell of reading. ~See also **read into, read out,** etc.

7.   **6.**

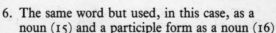

6. The same word but used, in this case, as a noun (15) and a participle form as a noun (16)
7. Cross reference to other forms and derivatives under separate entries

Some dictionaries also give the etymology of the word, explaining its derivation and evolution.

Armageddon	a class of battleship; a war that will end the world; the heavenly home for army generals
armoire	a lace shawl; a portable enamel bath; a large cupboard or wardrobe
arraign	to accuse before a court; to forcibly arrest; to hold under arrest pending bail
arriviste	a pushy self-seeker; a socialite thief; an immigrant refused entry to a country
asinine	haughty; darkly handsome; stupid
assuage	to irritate; to relieve; to roughen
atrophy	wasting away; malarial fever; blood clotting
attenuate	to lengthen; to make flat; to make thin
attrition	apologising to a court of law; the process of wearing away; automobile collision insurance
au fait	unacceptable; having expert knowledge; on the wrong side of the law
avuncular	like a kindly uncle; covered with pustules; good humoured only when under the influence of alcohol

B

Using the meanings given,
fill in the gaps.

(Answers page 88)

bad _ _ age	Teasing banter and repartee
b _ _ chanalian	Riotous and drunken revelry
Bakel _ _ _	An early heat-resistant synthetic resin
ba _ _ ful	Full of evil, deadly intent
balus _ _ ade	A banister supported by balusters
b _ _ dolatry	Worship of Shakespeare
bar mit _ _ _ h	Jewish ceremony admitting a boy as an adult member of the faith
baro _ _ e	Extravagant style of decoration or architecture
b _ _ hos	Descent from the sublime to the ridiculous or commonplace
bay _ u	Marshy, slow-running stream in America
b _ _ titude	Heavenly bliss
behemo _ _	A huge person, animal or object
bel c _ _ to	Virtuoso singing
be _ _ icose	Aggressive and warlike
be _ _ wether	One who takes the lead or initiative
bem _ _ ed	Bewildered and confused
ben _ _ n	Kindly, gentle and genial
besmi _ _ h	To soil, or sully the good name of someone

17

bête n _ _ re	Someone or something regarded with fear and loathing
b _ _ elot	A small but often valuable article
bie _ _ ial	Occurring every two years
b _ _ urcate	To divide into two, or forked
bij _ _	A small, valuable jewel or trinket
bi _ _ teral	Relating to two sides or parties
bin _ _ _	System of numbers using 2 as its base
b _ _ psy	Removal of tissue from a body for examination
b _ _ sé	Indifferent, apathetic and unresponsive through over-indulgence
bl _ _ ch	To flinch, to shrink back from something
bli _ _ ely	Cheerfully carefree
b _ _ a fi _ e	Genuinely, in good faith
b _ _ homie	Good-natured friendliness
bon viv _ _ _	One who loves food and drink
b _ _ eal	Of the north; northern countries and peoples
bo _ _ y	Overgrown with trees and shrubs
bour _ _ oisie	The middle classes
b _ _ _ lerise	To cut words and passages from a book on prudish grounds
bra _ _ adocio	Bragging, boasting
br _ _ se	To cook slowly in liquid in a closed pan
Brob _ _ _ nagian	Of gigantic proportions, from the country of giants in *Gulliver's Travels*
brou _ a _ a	A fuss, an uproar
brus _ _ e	Blunt in manner; rough and abrupt
b _ _ olic	Pastoral; relating to the countryside

b _ _ imia	Abnormal craving for food with bouts of overeating followed by self-induced vomiting
bump _ _ ous	Excessively and unpleasantly self-assertive
b _ _ geoning	Sprouting; starting to grow
bur _ _ p	Very coarse canvas or sacking
b _ _ _ ish	To polish and make smooth and shiny
bus _ _ _	A waiter's assistant
B _ _ onic	Romantically melancholic

Lovely and unlovely words

You can't help liking and disliking certain words. The romantic novelist Barbara Cartland professes to love the words **shimmering, moonlight** (naturally!), **rapture, pure, innocent, divine** and **God**. A poll conducted by the *US Literary Digest* came up with **illusion, mirage** and **azure** as the top three, followed by **celestial, quintessence, ravish, whisper, twilight, meander, lovely, evanescent, taffeta** and **mellifluous**. In Britain, the learned journal *Logophile* published the words most loved by celebrities; these included **pellucid, aquiline, lily, silken, alembic** (Bernard Levin); **spume, vanilla, dingle, hellebore, dusk, murmur, heirloom, treacle, chocolate, flummery** (Posy Simmonds); **mandragora, valerian, polysyllable, adamantine** and **cellardoor** (Jilly Cooper). And the word most disliked by readers of *The Times*? **Chomp** – closely followed by **fax**.

C

Which of the two meanings is correct?

(Answers page 89)

cabal	A group of plotters, or the brick lip on the top of a chimney stack
cabriole	A curved chair leg, or a horse-drawn carriage
cache	An old Indo-Chinese coin, or a hiding place
cajole	To persuade with flattery, or Indian cornmeal
calcareous	Containing calcium, or dental decay
callipygian	Ability to see in the dark, or having well-formed buttocks
callisthenics	Exercises for strength and beauty, or exercises to develop the lumbar muscles
calumny	A maliciously false statement, or a rude verse
camaraderie	A Parisian nightclub, or loyalty among comrades
campanology	The art of survival in the wilds, or the study of bell-ringing
canard	A false rumour, or a joke
candour	Openness and integrity, or hypocritical praise
cantankerous	Disagreeable and crotchety, or excessively cautious and thrifty

captious	Fearful of being imprisoned, or hard to please
carcanet	An inlaid jewel box, or a jewelled collar
carpal	Relating to the wrist, or relating to exotic fish
carte blanche	Advice to act quickly, or permission to act freely and unrestrained
cartel	An agreement between business interests to regulate output and prices, or an agreement between nations to exclude others
castellated	A special cigar wrapping, or castle-like
castigate	To chastise, or to beat severely
catalysis	Speeding up a chemical reaction with a substance that remains unchanged, or analysing the components of exhaust emissions
catamite	A boy prostitute, or the chief eunuch in a Turkish harem
catharsis	Curing medical problems by hypnosis, or purging emotional problems through dramatic re-enactment
catheter	A tube for draining fluids from the body, or a secret tunnel under a church
causerie	A chatty conversation or essay, or a group of people devoted to charity work
caveat emptor	Let the buyer have a choice, or let the buyer beware
cavil	To find fault, or to rush into things
celerity	Swiftness, or sourness
chancel	A circular window in a church, or the area around the altar reserved for the clergy
charlatan	An imposter, or a Scottish fortune-teller
chauvinism	Blind patriotism, or love of French art

chiaroscuro	Cherry brandy, or the visual effects of light and shade
chicanery	Coffee roasting, or trickery
chiffonier	A sideboard, usually with shelves and mirror above, or an elegant dressing-table, usually with a single drawer and oval mirror
chimera	An imagined monster or horror, or the patterns made by fire smoke
choleric	Tendency for chest complaints, or bad-tempered
chutzpah	A Hebrew lament, or cheerful audacity
cinéaste	A serious movie enthusiast, or a bitter taste
circa	Approximate, or 'within that century'
circumlocution	Travelling around the globe without crossing the equator, or a round-about way of talking
circumscribed	Removal of a toe, or to be restricted
clandestine	Love of bright lights and entertainment, or conducted in secrecy
clement	Mild and gentle, or wild and strong
cognoscenti	Connoisseurs, or principal male ballet dancers
colloquy	A dream that is remembered, or a dialogue
collude	To re-colonise a country, or to conspire, usually for dishonest purposes
comity	Friendliness, or extreme deviousness
complaisant	Freckled, or eager to please
concomitant	Partly incontinent, or in conjunction with
concupiscence	Sexual lust, or patronising
conflation	Blending two things together, or indigestion
consanguinity	Unlawful acts between humans and animals, or related by birth

contemn	To love nature, or to despise someone
contretemps	An awkward and embarrassing situation, or a contrary child
corpus delicti	The facts about a crime, or the preservation of a dead body for evidence

---

What is the longest word?

When Shakespeare used the word **honorificabilitudinitatibus** in *Love's Labour's Lost*, it held the record for the longest word in the English language for quite some time. It was overtaken in the 18th century by **floccinaucinihilipilification** (meaning the habitual estimation of the worthlessness of something) until challenged by the Mary Poppins' 34-letter **supercalifragilisticexpialidocious** in 1964, which even small children could get their tongues around. But both went down for the count in 1982 when the *Oxford English Dictionary* listed a lung disease calling for a 45-letter word: **pneumonoultramicroscopicsilicovolcanoconiosis**. Now it is reported that even **pn . . . osis** has been put in the shade by an 8,000-letter behemoth of a word that describes a protein derivative. Very impressive, but can it beat the word **smiles**? That's a word that has a mile between its first and last letters.

---

coruscate	To punish severely, or to glitter
costive	Cheating by altering prices, or constipated
coterie	An exclusive group of people sharing common interests, or a dance performed by four people
crapulous	Untidy, or given to overindulgent drinking and eating

crescendo	The loudest passage in a musical performance, or a gradual increase in sound and force
cruciform	Shaped like a cross, or crystalline
crustaceans	Oysters and mussels, or crabs and lobsters
cultivar	A plant originated by cultivation, or a Russian tea-drinking receptacle
cupidity	Dimpled, or inordinate desire to possess
cynosure	Centre of attraction, or justified cynicism
cytology	Study of the urinary tract, or the study of living cells

D

Choose the correct meaning.

(Answers page 89)

dado	early 20th-century surrealist movement; lower part of the wall of a room when differently decorated from upper part; a drink made from almonds
dalliance	flirting; sparkling; oratory
dearth	a plague; scarcity; frightening appearance
débâcle	an ornamented silver buckle; a large garden party; a complete rout and collapse
debilitate	to nourish; to wound; to weaken
déclassé	to come down socially; to act superior to one's status; to offer wine in the wrong glass
declivity	an abrupt drop; a gradual slope downwards; a sudden drop in barometric pressure
de facto	existing, though not legally; in defiance of the law; with the permission of the court
defalcate	to void; to misappropriate money; to sneeze
defenestration	to cut someone out of a will; to nullify an adoption; to throw someone out of a window

dégagé	free and easy; amorous; absentminded
déjà vu	old fashioned; a person acquainted with witchcraft; the illusion of having previously experienced a present event
deleterious	noxious; extremely sweet; wholesome
delphic	of dark appearance; always smiling; ambiguous
demagoguery	hatred of religion; emotional, prejudiced oratory; urge to degrade others
demi-monde	objects and clothing made in the 1920s; a woman of dubious character; a jewelled cloche hat
demotic	belonging to the common people; staring wildly; student of the black arts
demurrer	an objection; a writ; a demand for payment
dénouement	a foiled elopement; a military surrender; the unravelling and solution of a mystery
depilatory	for preventing bleeding; for removing hair; for reducing perspiration
de rigueur	required by etiquette; demanded by regulation; suggested by a close friend
desiccate	to chop finely; to dry; to shred
desultory	fish able to live in fresh and sea water; casual and unmethodical; to feel inferior
determinism	belief that determination will solve all tasks; belief that the father more than the mother determines their child's features; belief that external forces and not heredity determine an individual's actions and fate
dextral	left-handed; right-handed; colour blind

dialectic	patient with kidney failure; logical and analytical argument; a scientific religion
dichotomy	second hymn of a church service; operation on joints of the foot; divided into two
didactic	inclined to teach; inclined to avoid problems; inclined to depend on others
dilatory	slow; fast; standing immobile
dipsomaniac	pickpocket; cat burglar; alcoholic
discommode	to take another name; to inconvenience someone; to take away a person's passport
discrete	detached and separate; composed of a single substance; massive
disparage	discourage; destroy; depreciate
dissemble	to hide one's intentions; to hinder; to argue
distrain	to seize goods in payment for a debt; to obtain a legal claim on a person's wages; to purchase a distressed mortgage or lease
diurnal	pertaining to daytime; pertaining to the night; pertaining to leap year
divertissement	advertising that is repeated; a piece of music for the cello; an entertainment
doctrinaire	dogmatic devotion to a theory; a senior medical doctor; a training hospital
dolorous	indolent; boring; full of pain and grief
double entendre	two theatre tickets for the price of one; a *risqué* ambiguous statement or joke; highly gifted and artistic twins
doughty	formidably brave; glum appearance; very untidy
doyen	a Jewish professor; a folk music band; the senior member of a profession or group

draconian	breathing fire; harsh; death by quicksand
drugget	a coarse woven mat; a square-shaped pill; a parlour where opium is smoked
dudgeon	optimism; sullen resentment; disappointment
duodenum	a digestive gland; the hearing organ of the ear; the first portion of the small intestine

Johnson's dictionary

Although not the first, Dr Samuel Johnson's *A Dictionary of the English Language* was certainly the most influential dictionary until the appearance of the *New English Dictionary* – later called the *Oxford* – between 1884 and 1928. Nine years in the making with the combined labours of Johnson and six helpers, the massive dictionary defined 43,000 words and was published in 1755 to become the ultimate reference book on English for a century and a half. Yet Johnson's dictionary is far from being a dry academic tome; it positively bristles with its author's quirky personality, quite a few errors and inconsistencies, brilliantly concise definitions and – Johnson being Johnson – a few jokes. One of these was his definition of oats: '*A grain which in England is generally given to horses, but in Scotland supports the people.*' The Scots got their own back with the riposte: 'Johnson has explained why Scotland has the most beautiful women, and England the most beautiful horses.'

E

Using the meanings given,
fill in the gaps.

(Answers page 90)

ebull _ _ nt	Full of high spirits and enthusiasm
e _ ful _ ent	Shining brightly
egal _ _ arian	One who believes in human equality
eg _ _ entric	Self-centred
egr _ gious	Flagrantly appalling
éla _	Panache
elegi _ c	Melancholic and mournful
ele _ _ antine	Huge, unwieldy
éli _ e	The best
El _ sian	Blissful, like a paradise
eman _ _ e	To issue or flow from
e _ _ ncipate	To set free
emas _ _ late	To weaken, to deprive of masculine properties
emb _ _ go	To restrict or prohibit
embolis _	The blocking of an artery or vein by a blood clot
embr _ onic	Undeveloped
eme _ date	To correct by removing errors and faults
emo _ _ ient	A preparation that softens and soothes
em _ lument	A payment for services

empa _ _ y	Identification with another's feelings
empiri _ _ l	Conclusions based on experiment, experience or observation
encom _ um	A citation of very high praise
en _ _ mic	Found in a particular place; indigenous
ener _ ate	To weaken
enf _ nt te _ _ ible	An embarrassing child
eng _ _ der	To cause or bring about something
enig _ _	Something unexplainable
en _ oin	To order or instruct someone to do something
en _ ui	Listlessness and boredom
enor _ ity	An atrocity of outrageous proportions
enunci _ _ e	To articulate clearly
e _ _ emera	Something short-lived
ep _ cure	A person devoted to sensual pleasures, especially eating and drinking
epig _ _ m	A witty saying or short verse
equit _ _ le	Fair and just
equi _ ocal	Ambiguous, uncertain
ergon _ _ ics	The study of working conditions and efficiency
ero _ enous	Sexually sensitive
ersat _	An artificial or inferior substitute
eruc _ a _ ion	Belching
er _ dite	Well-read and well-informed
eso _ eric	Something intelligible only to an initiated few
esp _ it de cor _ s	Spirit of loyalty and devotion to a group to which one belongs
et _ os	The inherent characteristics of a culture or organisation
etymol _ gy	The origin and history of words

30

e _ genics	The science of improving hereditary characteristics
e _ logise	To praise highly
eu _ _ emism	The substitution of a bland or pleasant expression for a disagreeable one

---

Word playtime

Expanding your vocabulary need not be drudgery: far from it. For about as long as words have existed we've played games with them – and as far as English is concerned, playing word games (crosswords, scrabble, puzzle books and all the rest) is an amusing way in which to put more muscle into your word power. Here are a couple of quickies:

- What do the words **cauliflower**, **behaviour**, **equation** and **mendacious** have in common?
- What single four-letter word is used in baseball, basketball, boxing, fishing, football, golf and hockey?

---

eupho _ i _	The heady feeling of supreme well-being
Eur _ _ ian	Of mixed European and Asian blood
e _ than _ sia	Painless killing of terminally ill or old people
evan _ _ cent	Fading away
exa _ erbate	To irritate and make worse
e _ coriate	To remove the skin
excul _ _ te	To free from blame
exe _ rable	Detestable
exeg _ _ is	A critical explanation
e _ emplary	Someone or something so good as to be worth imitating

exor _ ise	To drive out evil or evil spirits
expa _ iate	To speak or write at considerable length
expa _ _ iate	To expel someone from a country by force
exp _ _ te	To atone or make amends
expr _ pri _ te	To dispossess an owner of something, usually property, often for public use
ex _ ur _ ate	To remove supposedly offensive passages (from a book etc.)
ex _ irpate	To exterminate

F

Which of the two meanings
is correct?

(*Answers page 90*)

facile	Something accomplished easily but without depth, or a smooth liar
factotum	A 'jack of all trades' sort of servant, or the daily collection of workers' 'clock-on' cards
fait accompli	An accomplished fact, or a loyal but unwilling accomplice to a crime
fallacy	A Papal law, or a false belief or argument
farrago	An Indian grain, or a confused mixture
fascism	Authoritarian government, or an art movement
fastidious	Well-dressed, or hard to please
fatuous	Complacently stupid, or complacently overweight
faux pas	Cunning like a fox, or a social indiscretion
fealty	Bravery, or loyalty
febrile	Lukewarm liquid, or inclined to be feverish
feckless	A person without purpose or principles, or a horse impossible to train
fecund	fertile, or one-millionth of a minute

The Oxford English Dictionary – The OED

When Sir James Murray began to compile the first
OED in 1879, he constructed in his garden an
iron shed in which there were over 1,000
pigeonholes in readiness for several million slips
of paper which would be stored in them. On these
slips would be entered definitions and citations of
words – the contributions of many thousands of
amateur lexicographers from around the world.
The marathon of compiling and defining,
proofreading and publishing the dictionary
occupied the rest of Murray's life; when he died
in 1915 it had only reached the letter T. Another
13 years were needed to complete it and, with
16,000 pages in 10 volumes, it finally appeared in
1928, to be followed by the first supplement in
1933. Subsequently, other supplements were
published, concluding with S–Z in 1986.

The new, *Second Edition* – the *OED2* – was
published in 1989 with just under half a million
words, illustrated by 2.5 million quotations,

felicitous	Charming and well-suited, or lit with a luminous glow
feral	Stained with iron, or in a wild state
fervid	Diseased, or impassioned
filibuster	A type of firework that ends with a cannonade, or the technique of delaying the progress of legislation by prolonged speechmaking
flaccid	Flabby, or milky
flews	The canals that feed a watermill, or the pendant jowls of certain breeds of dogs
flippant	Frivolous, or skipping
florescence	Blossoming of a plant, or glowing in the dark
florid	Ruddy or highly embellished, or the side of a coin which bears a date

packed into 20 weighty volumes. There, any similarities with Murray's dictionary end, for the *OED2* is a product of the computer age, and users possessing the right hardware can buy the entire work on CD–ROM for £500, or a third of the price of the books.

Capturing the original dictionary and the supplements electronically, while incorporating a further 30,000 new words and quotations, was an awesome undertaking requiring an estimated 500 person-years and an accuracy rate of just 4.5 errors per 10,000 keystrokes. The result is breathtaking; users can 'interrogate' the electronic version and extract complex information in seconds – information that might take days and even months to find in the book version. It can confirm, for example, that the only common English words ending in **-shion** are, astonishingly, **cushion** and **fashion**; and the only words ending in **-gry** are **angry** and **hungry**. Not many amateur lexicographers know that.

flout	To show off, or treat with contempt
foible	A small trinket, or a personal weakness
forensic	Pertaining to law courts, or pertaining to an autopsy
fortuitous	Ability to read future events, or accidental
fractious	Restless and irritable, or out of control
friable	Able to be cooked in oil, or crumbly
fulgent	Bright and dazzling, or the smell of death
fulminate	To explode, or a slow burning that causes fumes
fulsome	Gluttony, or excessive and insincere
fundamentalism	Belief in the literal truth of sacred texts, or belief that not only humans but all creatures have souls

furbelow   Flouncy trimming on clothing, or the line with which sailors measure the depth of water

furlough   Ten furlongs, or leave of absence

G

Select the correct usage.

(Meanings page 90)

gaffe He finished off the shark with a gaffe. He later apologised for his gaffe.

gambit Flashing a big smile at a man was her usual gambit. As he entered the cellar he had to stoop under the gambit.

gamut His mind raced through the gamut of possibilities. The ugly little gamut came up and swore at me.

garrulous Something she'd eaten made her queasy and garrulous. The more he drank, the louder and more garrulous he became.

gauche The artist presented her with a framed gauche. The young girl was beautiful but gauche.

gazebo He sat musing in the gazebo. At last he had the fleeing gazebo in his sights.

gefilte fish They all congratulated her on her gefilte fish. He'd been fishing all day and had caught only three gefilte fish and a small salmon.

genuflect As she entered, she genuflected

briefly towards the altar. The three-year sentence gave him ample time to genuflect upon his crime.

germane
Her hair shone germane in the moonlight. He insisted that the financial situation was germane to the argument.

gerrymander
The sitting candidate realised too late that the gerrymander would cost him the election. The gang boss threatened to gerrymander the FBI by fleeing to a neighbouring state.

gestation
The average gestation time for a heavy meal is five hours. It was obvious that the mare's gestation was in its final weeks.

gesundheit
'*Gesundheit!*' he said, raising his glass. '*Gesundheit!*', he swore, and sat down, frustrated.

gigolo
You could tell by his effeminate manner that he was a gigolo. She had plenty of money and a string of eager gigolos.

glutinous
The plant trapped insects in its glutinous nectary. He came up and spoke to my aunt in his usual glutinous manner.

gobbet
The starving prisoners clamoured for the gobbets of flesh. His body hung there for days beneath the evil, creaking gobbet.

gobbledegook
Among Lewis Carroll's creations were the Snark, the Boojum, the Cheshire Cat and the Gobbledegook. The memo was utter gobbledegook.

gourmandise   The factory was built to gourmandise milk into cheese. Her dream was to gourmandise on fancy Swiss chocolates.

grandiose   The garden party was a grandiose affair. He was always grandiose with his money.

New words

The 'G' section might well have concluded with the word **gurney**, a wheeled stretcher used for transporting patients. **Gurney** is just one of an estimated 3,000 or so new words created every year, and after a decade or so its usage is sufficiently widespread as to guarantee a degree of permanence. Words are constantly joining and leaving the language. Words like **freet** (a proverb), **frim** (vigorous and healthy) and **frayne** (to ask or enquire) expire from under-use to make way for hundreds of new words on our lips like **bimbo** and **yobbo**, **gazundered** and **software**, **fax** and **filofax**. But not all new words make the grade; the square television aerial called the **squarial** had such a short life it could be termed an **emphemarial**, and terms like number-crunching and bean-counting are likely to remain in limbo for quite a while before acquiring lexical respectability. That need not prevent us using them, however; if we used only dictionary words in our everyday speech and writing our vocabulary would seem very stilted indeed. So *vivat* **pecs**, **bar code** and **couch potato**!

---

gratuitous   Not all the diners were gratuitous to the waiters. The movie was marred by the scenes of gratuitous violence.

gravamen

The gravamen of the case was the premeditated nature of the attack. The vicar finally delivered his gravamen to the happy couple.

gregarious

He was a gregarious person and invariably grew irritable when alone. When the gregarious mood hit him he would lie and wait for some casual prey.

gumption

The brick pillars were topped with weathered stone gumptions. The teacher told them that with a bit of gumption they could do anything.

Choose the correct meaning.

(Answers page 91)

habeas corpus	murder case lacking a body; demand for a prisoner to appear before the court; appeal to dismiss a case through lack of evidence
habitué	regular visitor; drug addict; well dressed
hackneyed	transported by horse-drawn carriage; stale and trite; tired and listless
hagiography	a stream of invective; a catalogue of complaints; a biography that regards its subject as a saint
ha-ha	a sunken fence; a fountain; a summer house
halcyon	peaceful and pleasant; a thick crayon used for stage makeup; the fringe on a carpet
halitosis	body odour; smelly feet; bad breath
hapless	clumsy; angry and irritable; unfortunate and unlucky
harbinger	someone or something that foretells an event; a rowing boat used for hunting whales; a species of honey-eating bird
hector	to shout; to act strangely; to bully

Homophones

When the crate was opened, out stepped a gnu, and the rest of the zoo wondered what the new gnu knew. The last three words are **homophones**: words pronounced the same but different in meaning and spelling. There are hundreds of them lying in wait for the unwary. Here are just a few to watch out for:

air, ere, heir, eyre   aisle, I'll, isle
born, borne, bourne   braise, brays, braze
by, buy, bye   cents, scents, sense
cord, cored, chord   eau, oh, owe
ewe, yew, you   flew, flu, flue
heal, heel, he'll   gnu, knew, new
holey, holy, wholly   knows, noes, nose
load, lode, lowed   meat, meet, mete
nay, née, neigh   oar, or, ore
pair, pare, pear   peak, peek, pique
prays, praise, preys   rain, reign, rein
road, rode, rowed   seas, sees, seize
teas, tease, tees   to, too, two
vain, vane, vein

The different meanings of homophones and many other look-alikes and grammatical mischief-makers will be found in another *One Hour Wordpower* book, *Word Check: Using Words Correctly*.

hegemony	property passing from mother to children; the dominance of one country over another; the state's right to tax citizens
heinous	horse-loving; wicked; rural
hellebore	a rude and tiresome person; a group of plants; a type of ship's figurehead

heresy	an unorthodox belief; a wicked lie; a traitorous act
heterogeneous	of the same kind; of different kind; of either sex
heuristic	the capacity to inquire and find out; an obsession with time; lover of holy things
hiatus	a break or gap; a summer holiday; hiccups
Hibernian	pertaining to Scotland; pertaining to Ireland; pertaining to the Isle of Man
hindsight	all-round vision; the part of a gunsight nearest the eye; wise after the event
histology	study of organic tissue; study of ancient burial sites; study of hay fever
hogmanay	last day of the year; New Year's Day; a Scottish dance
hoi polloi	upper class; common people; highbrow
hologram	printing by means of gelatin; a ghostly vision of Christ; a three-dimensional photographic image
homogeneous	all the same kind; all different; mixed
honorarium	a minor award to civil servants; a payment; a collection of medals
hortatory	pertaining to clocks and time-keeping; sleepwalking condition; giving encouragement
hubris	arrogant conceit or pride; a sepia-like colour; an oil obtained from the sperm whale
humanism	a system concerned with kindness to animals; a system concerned with the needs of man; a system concerned with selective breeding
humdrum	an Indian grain; dull and tedious; irritating
hydrology	the study of water; the study of ferns; the study of the upper atmosphere

hygrometer	measures moisture in the air; measures air pressure; measures impurities in the air
hyperbole	exaggeration; a huge arena; hypnotherapy

icono _ _ ast	One who attacks established doctrines and beliefs
i _ iomatic	Speech and expressions characteristic of a region or country
idios _ ncrasy	A personal habit or peculiarity of manner
id _ _ atry	Worship of idols and images
ignom _ _ y	Disgrace and dishonour
imbrogl _ _	A complex and confused state of affairs
imm _ late	To kill by sacrifice, usually by fire
immu _ ed	Imprisoned, walled in
im _ utable	Unchanging and unalterable
i _ passe	An insurmountable obstacle or situation
implac _ ble	Unrelenting and not to be appeased
imp _ _ tune	To demand urgently and persistently
imprimat _ r	A mark of approval
improm _ tu	Off hand, without preparation
impu _ n	To dispute the validity or truth of an argument, or challenge the word of someone
in _ _ vertent	Unintentionally careless

45

incip _ ent	In the first stages
incogni _ o	Avoiding recognition by disguise or by assuming another name
incul _ ate	To impress on the mind by repetition or force
inc _ mbent	The holder of a position or office; a moral obligation under the circumstances
ind _ _ nity	Security against damage or loss
indigen _ _ s	Native to a particular country or region
indig _ _ t	Destitute
ineffab _ _	Too overwhelming to be expressed in words
inel _ ctable	Inevitable and unavoidable
ine _ orable	Unmoved, unbending and unyielding
in _ ra dig	Beneath one's dignity
in _ énue	A naive and artless yong girl
ingen _ ous	Open, candid and frank
ini _ ical	Hostile and behaving like an enemy
inna _ e	Inborn
inno _ uous	Harmless
innuen _ o	An oblique hint or suggestion, usually derogatory
insa _ ubrious	Unhealthy
ins _ dious	Subtly intent on deceiving or betraying
insouc _ ant	Careless and unconcerned
inter ali _	Among other things
interdi _ t	To authoritatively forbid
interne _ ine	Mutually destructive
inter _ tice	A small space or crack between two things
int _ ansigent	Uncompromising and irreconcilable
intr _ _ sic	Essential, inherent

in _ _ overt	Someone interested in his own thoughts, feelings and actions
invei _ h	To verbally denounce
invi _ ious	Provoking anger and resentment
i _ ascible	Easily excited and angered
i _ _ evocable	Incapable of being revoked or repealed

Janus words

What's the difference between dusting tomato plants for mildew and dusting the grand piano? The same word is describing two completely opposite actions: adding dust and removing it. **Dusting** is known as a Janus word – a verbal hermaphrodite that can have either of two opposite meanings. Such words are fascinating: think about **sanction**, **fast**, **handicap**, **cleave** and **draw** (when you draw the curtains are you opening them or closing them?) – all of them have opposite meanings.

Close cousins of Janus words are words that appear to be opposites but which share the same meaning: **inflammable** and **flammable**, **bend** and **unbend**, **passive** and **impassive**. You might also like to ponder such contradictory terms as **getting up** and **getting down** from the dinner table; and **slowing up** and **slowing down** in a car.

J

Which of the two meanings
is correct?

(*Answers page 91*)

jaundiced	A prejudicial attitude, or an untrue statement
jejune	Bright and sparkling, or immature, insipid and uninteresting
jeopardy	Exposure to danger or loss, or a pattern with wide stripes used for camouflage
jeremiad	An extremely unlucky person, or a lament
jettison	To throw things overboard, or to crash a boat into a dock
jihad	A crusade for or against a belief or faith, or the ruling council of a Muslim state
jingoism	A compulsion to tell jokes, or aggressive patriotism
jocose	Humorous and facetious, or red-faced
joie de vivre	Joy of being alive, or a delight in aggression
junta	A ruling council, often dictatorial, or a South American dictator
juvenescence	Loss of memory, or becoming young again
juxtapose	To place something against something else, or to cover something up with something else

Know what I mean?

'Er . . . you know . . . those silver things you put three candles in . . . ummm . . .' **Candelabra**, of course! How many times do we accurately describe something but can't remember its name? Here are some definitions of fairly common things; see if you can supply their names.

1. The plaster moulding used to disguise the join between wall and ceiling
2. The pedal you push when you change gear in a car
3. The raised-dot alphabet for the blind
4. Those timber or concrete walls that run across the foreshore down to the sea
5. The small Victorian lady's writing desk with drawers down one side
6. The theory that divides the brain and skull into sections denoting mental and emotional characteristics
7. The heavy farm horse that is dark brown with white markings
8. The signs much used by astrologers
9. The craze in pubs for singing popular songs to taped musical accompaniment
10. Those men that wave frantically at horse races

(*answers page 95*)

K

Select the correct usage.

(Meanings page 91)

karma
He lay on the ground, wrapped in a bright red karma. He sat there, dejected, convinced his karma was not good.

kibbutz
She looked healthy and radiant after her year at the kibbutz. The Prime Minister's problem was that he could not control the ruling kibbutz.

kitsch
It was well known that as an artist he produced nothing but kitsch. As a family friend, he undertook to act as the children's kitsch.

kleptomaniac
After a dozen convictions for theft she was finally diagnosed as a kleptomaniac. His sleepwalking confirmed him as a kleptomaniac.

kosher
The new woollen kosher fitted her perfectly. Three passengers on the flight had ordered kosher meals.

kowtow
He had never seen a Chinese person with the traditional kowtow. He hated to kowtow to his employers in the big house.

kudos
They would spend hours playing kudos. His sales figures brought him plenty of kudos.

Litotes

Litotes (pronounced *ly-to-tees*) is an ancient rhetorical device used to express understatement, as in: 'He was not totally displeased', meaning 'He was very pleased'. Another common example is 'not bad', meaning 'pretty good'. Litotes are also useful for expressing a 'not-completely-opposite' thought; to say that someone is 'not unhappy' means not that they are happy, but that they are content and satisfied. Litotes you'll constantly come across include 'not unwelcome', 'not unlike' and 'not a few': all part of our rich but often contradictory vocabulary.

L

Choose the correct meaning.

(Answers page 92)

lachrymose	oversweet; ready to weep; muscular
laconic	economical (of speech); casual; given to boasting
lacuna	a gap or blank; the centre of a lens; the hazy ring around the moon
laity	clergy; laymen; male members of a choir
laissez-faire	restricting immigration; over-willingness to accept harsh laws; policy of non-intervention
lambent	easily bent; softly flickering; blue-tinted
lampoon	ship's lantern; a satiric attack; a whale
languor	lack of energy and enthusiasm; a sexually inviting look; semi-consciousness
largess	water that gathers in the hull of a ship; a type of peach; a generous gift, usually money
lascivious	lustful; given to laughter; blood-red
latent	existing but not noticeable; just prior to boiling point; triangular sail
lateral	towards the top; towards a bottom edge; to or from the side
laudable	sanctified; praiseworthy; drugged with opium

legerdemain	folklore; sleight of hand; deep knowledge
leitmotif	a recurring theme; German subway system; a motiveless crime
lèse-majesté	royal divorce; bending the knee; high treason
lethargic	lead poisoning; drowsy and apathetic; shortage of breath
libido	Italian teenager; the sexual drive; a wash basin used for shampooing hair
libretto	text of an opera or vocal work; soprano section of an operatic choir; interval during an opera
licentious	sexually unrestrained; operating without a licence; involved in piracy
lickerish	inspired playing of the clarinet; wet and sloppy; lustful and lecherous
lionize	to threaten; to treat someone as a celebrity; to covet the adulation of crowds
lissom	persuasive speech; golden haired; supple
locum tenens	a professional substitute; an alcoholic delirium; a woodworker's tool
logorrhea	disease of the gums; abnormal talkativeness; theory of numbers
longueur	train of a wedding dress; a vain person; a tedious passage in a book or play
loquacious	talkative; semi-naked; having red-rimmed eyes
Lothario	seducer of women; swarthy; extremely strong
louche	charming; effeminate; shady and devious
lubricious	charming in manner; outrageously effeminate; oily and lecherous
lugubrious	mournful; lewd; vain
lumpen	people who are overweight; deprived and degraded; gentlemen farmers

53

Which of the two meanings
is correct?

(Answers page 92)

macerate	To regurgitate food, or to soften by soaking
Machiavellian	Unscrupulous scheming, or achieving political ends by use of explosives

Mallemaroking

For a ship to be icebound these days is something
of a rare event; either that, or the newsworthiness
of icebound ships is rated about zero. But if, say,
a ship *were* icebound, one would think that the
sailors on the unfortunate vessel would be a
downcast lot, glumly counting off the weeks and
months to the arrival of the thaw. However, a
word exists that suggests we are wrong. That
word is **mallemaroking**, meaning the carousing of
seamen aboard icebound ships. Alone among
dictionaries, it seems, *Chambers Twentieth Century
Dictionary* has carried the word over many years
through several editions, so there must be a use
for it. Perhaps a clandestine but booming travel
business exists, flying tourists to ships icebound
in the Arctic Circle for a good old mallemaroking.
Or perhaps *Chambers* is having us all on.

macrocosm	A universal whole, or a thin sliver of tissue for microscopic examination
magisterial	Dictatorial, or a liking for legal robes
magnum opus	A champagne bottle which holds 6 magnums of champagne, or the greatest work of an artist, composer or writer
maladroit	Awkward and clumsy, or a love of reptiles
malaise	A tropical disease, or a vague feeling of uneasiness and discomfort
malapropism	Using the wrong cutlery, or misusing words
mal de mer	A sea delicacy, or sea sickness
malfeasance	Lying under oath, or official misconduct
Malthusian	The theory that populations will always outstrip the food supply unless checked, or that the world consumes resources faster than it can create or replace them
maudlin	Tearfully sentimental, or easily convinced
maunder	To receive alms on Maundy Thursday, or to wander incoherently
mea culpa	'The drink is poisoned', or 'It's my fault'
megalomania	Fear of spots, or delusions of grandeur
megrim	A severe headache and depression, or a horrific dream
mélange	A mixture, or a milk jelly dessert
mêlée	A lady's long silk dressing gown, or a confused fight
mellifluous	Sweet to the taste, or sweetly flowing
ménage	A household, or a stable of horses
mendacious	Prone to lying and deception, or miserly
mendicant	A holistic doctor, or a beggar

mephitic	Offensive to the nose, or a substance that makes the eyes water
meretricious	Annoyingly repetitive, or vulgarly attractive
mesmerise	To hypnotise, or to cure illnesses by immersing in ice or icy water
metabolism	The bodily process that converts food to energy, or the theory that base metals like lead can be converted to gold
métier	One's natural vocation, or a group of art students
metronymic	Music with a steady beat, or a name or qualities derived from a maternal ancestor
micron	A unit for measuring the weight of stars, or one-millionth of a metre
micturate	To preserve crystals in oil, or to urinate frequently
milieu	Environment, or large, ornate wardrobe
millennium	One thousand years, or the year o
minatory	Threatening, or abnormally tall
misanthropy	Compulsive hoarding, or hatred of mankind
miscegenation	Lack of birth control, or racial interbreeding
misnomer	A mistaken or wrongly applied name, or an unnamed child
misogyny	Hatred of women, or fear of marriage
mnemonic	An eight-line poem, or a device to help the memory
moiety	A half share, or prone to subservience
moiré	A unit of radioactivity, or a wavy-patterned fabric
monograph	A black and white computer screen, or a treatise on a single subject
moratorium	A temporary suspension of an activity, or a burial ground for non-believers

56

moribund	Coming to an end, or highly fertile
mot juste	A misleading summing up by a judge to a jury, or the perfectly fitting word or phrase
mufti	A very hot curry, or ordinary clothes worn by a serviceman off duty
mundane	Ordinary and matter-of-fact, or a person who has a deficient sense of humour
myocardiogram	A record of waves from the frontal lobe of the brain, or a record of the muscular activity of the heart
myopia	A propensity to weep, or short-sightedness

N

Using the meanings given,
fill in the gaps.

(Answers page 92)

nad _ r	The lowest possible point
n _ scent	Beginning to exist or develop
nebul _ _ s	Vague and indistinct
n _ crop _ y	Examination of a dead body
ne _ arious	Wicked and evil
neg _ s	A drink of wine, hot water, sugar and spices
n _ m _ sis	Retributive justice
neol _ _ ism	The coining of a new word or giving a new meaning to an existing word
neoph _ te	A novice or beginner
ne _ hritis	Inflammation of the kidneys
nepoti _ _	Favouring one's relatives, especially in relation to jobs and positions
ne _ us	Something that joins or links
nih _ lism	A doctrine that holds that nothing has value or meaning, and rejects all traditional values, beliefs and institutions
n _ _ some	Offensive and disgusting, especially a smell
no _ age	The period of legal minority

The nous on dous

How many words end in **-dous**? Surprisingly, less than a dozen. But if you leave out the rare (**nefandous** – unmentionable), the archaic (**plumbous** – resembling lead) and the scientific (**steganopodous** – webbed toes) there are only four in common use. See if you can identify them:

The climb up Everest was h – – – – dous
The weather, though, was h – – – – – dous
The views were simply s – – – – – dous
And the thrill of it all was t – – – – – dous

(answers page 96)

non _ _ alant	Indifferent, calm and cool
non se _ _ itur	An illogical conclusion or statement
nost _ um	A dubious cure-all
n _ bile	A woman of marriageable age
nug _ _ ory	Unimportant, and not worth anything

O

Choose the correct meaning.

(Answers page 92)

obdurate	determined; stubborn; pleasant and obliging
obeisance	a gesture of homage; traitorous; obstinate
obfuscate	to paint in bright colours; to swear; to confuse or obscure
obloquy	a prayer for the dead; evasive language; abusive and reproachful language
obsequious	loyal; servile; gentle
obsolescent	becoming outdated; obsolete; easily broken
obstreperous	unruly and uncontrollable; untrustworthy; making slanderous statements
obviate	to speed things up; to criticise harshly; to make unnecessary
occidental	an oriental; a westerner; a South American
occlude	to mist over; to shut out; to ooze out
odium	hatred; a very bad smell; a rare metal
odontologist	cares for the feet; cares for the nose; cares for the teeth

Onomatopoeic words

These are words that imitate the sounds associated with an action or object, like **buzz**, **fizz**, **crackle**, **pop**, **whoosh**, **ping-pong**, **bubble**, **croak**, **cuckoo**, **sizzle**, and so on. Onomatopoeia is a useful tool for writers and poets who use it for effects, and it is of course the lifeblood of comic strips with their **WHAM! KER-AASHH! KA-ZUNK!**

oenologist	an expert in conversion of crude oil; an expert in wine and winemaking; an expert in soapmaking
oeuvre	a dish of quails' eggs; a list of soldiers killed in a battle; the whole work of a writer or artist
oligarchy	an unbroken line of female descendants; a government controlled by a privileged few; a communal olive grove in Greece
omniscient	knowing everything; being ruled by astrology; fear of the dark
opprobrium	disgrace; a dark place; an eye disease
oracular	roughly elliptical; prophetic; squinting
orotund	of spherical proportions; pertaining to apes and monkeys; eloquent and pompous speech
ossified	turned into paste; into bone; into rubber
ostensibly	seemingly; obviously; incautiously
ostentatious	silent and secretive; pretentious and showy; using bright, dazzling colours
osteopathy	treatment using water and sea products; treatment using nerve stimulation; treatment using massage and bone manipulation

otiose	useless and futile; fat and lazy; slow and lumbering
outré	mannish; fashionable; eccentric
overt	hidden and secret; open and public; shy and retiring

Pairs – of the dangerous kind

The word that is emerging for words that are easily confused is, not surprisingly, **confusables**. A common practice seems to be, 'when in doubt, leave them out', which is a pity because many so-called **confusables** are decidedly useful in everyday speech and writing. Here are just a few:

compulsive,   deprecate, depreciate
   compulsory   flout, flaunt
enormous, enormity   ingenious, ingenuous
implicit, explicit   militate, mitigate
loan, lend   noisome, noisy
licence, license   official, officious
obsolete, obsolescent   perquisite,
parameter, perimeter   prerequisite

and the list goes on. Even **its/it's** is these days regarded as a dangerous pair. An important aspect of building a more muscular vocabulary is to know the precise meanings of words, especially confusables. *Word Check: Using Words Correctly*, another book in this series, is a concise and friendly guide.

P

Which of the two meanings is correct?

(Answers page 93)

paediatrician	A specialist in bone diseases, or a specialist in children's diseases
palaver	A drawn-out discussion, or a Mexican-Indian woven cape
palpable	Evident and obvious, or barely eatable
panacea	A universal remedy, or wishful thinking
panache	Dash and verve, or a vague ache
Panglossian	Optimistic, or self-defeating
panegyric	Any bitter medicine, or an elaborate and very flattering expression of praise
panjandrum	A Punjabi feast, or a self-important official
pantheism	The doctrine that the universe is a manifestation of God, or the theory that all souls exist until eternity
paparazzi	A long row of marble columns, or tenacious freelance photographers of celebrities
paradigm	A model example, or a tongue-twisting phrase
paragon	A person held up to ridicule, or a model of excellence

63

parameter	An outermost limit, or variable constants used to determine a mathematical problem
paramour	An occasional lover, or the lover of a married man or woman
paranoia	Fear of criticism or attack, or delusions of persecution or grandeur
paraphrase	A restatement in different words intended to clarify, or a passage rewritten to hide its true meaning
pariah	Head of a tribe, or a social outcast
pari mutuel	A banking system that guarantees depositors a fixed interest rate, or a betting system that divides the total stakes among the winners
parlous	Embittered, or perilous
parsimony	A church endowment, or stinginess
parvenu	A newly rich social upstart, or a leading patron of the arts
passé	Up to the minute, or behind the times
pastiche	A work that imitates the style of another, or a slow movement for orchestral strings
paterfamilias	Male head of a household, or the collective uncles of a family
pathogenic	Pertaining to autopsies, or capable of causing disease
patina	Circumference of the retina of the eye, or an oxidised layer
patisserie	A shop selling pastries, or preserved meats
patrial	Pertaining to a person's country of birth, or a person with an unknown father

patrician	A fluent speaker of French, Italian and Spanish, or an aristocrat
Pecksniffian	An admirer of the works of Charles Dickens, or a hypocrite who advocates moral behaviour but who acts otherwise
pectorals	Chest muscles, or stomach muscles
pedagogue	A windy orator, or a school-teacher
pedantry	Excessive attention to rules and details, or the relentless pursuit of debtors
peignoir	A clasp to pull a woman's hair back, or a long, loose woman's negligee or dressing gown
pejorative	Disparaging and derogatory, or pompous
pellucid	Clear and transparent, or pearl-like
percipient	Rude and abrupt, or quick to see and understand
peregrination	A journey, or travelling in circles
peremptory	Cautious and hesitant, or decisive and final
perennial	Annually, or everlastingly
perfunctory	Careless and half-hearted, or vigorous
peripatetic	Prone to indigestion, or always travelling
periphrasis	Roundabout speech or writing, or obsession with words
pernicious	Irritating, or harmful
peroration	A memorial address, or the summing up at the end of a speech

perquisite	Unearned money or benefit, or a service that is required before a payment is made
persiflage	Frivolous banter, or embarrassing flattery
perspicacious	Unduly suspicious, or having the ability to understand things clearly
pertinacious	Cheeky, or stubbornly persistent
philanderer	A womaniser, or a travelling salesman
philistine	A person indifferent to the arts and learning, or someone who attacks established values
phlegmatic	Pessimistic, or stolidly calm and unexcitable
physiognomy	The study of cranial bumps and depressions, or a person's facial features
picayune	Petty and niggling, or bright and sparkling
pied-à-terre	A temporary or secondary apartment, or a dish featuring snails
pinnate	A flagless flagpole, or having the shape and arrangement of a feather
pixilated	Slightly dotty, or obsessed with garden gnomes
placebo	A substance given in place of real medicine, or a glass-walled garden summer house
plagiarism	Falsely attributing modern imitations as works of the old masters, or stealing and using another's ideas, inventions or writings and passing them off as one's own work

plangent	A deep and resounding noise, or a small, square-shaped pill
Platonic	A blood-bond between two men, or spiritual and non-sensual
plebeian	One who pleads before a court, or common and vulgar
plenary	Complete and absolute, or intermediate
plethora	Superabundance, or an operation for gallstones
plutocracy	Rule by the wealthy, or rule by the ignorant
podiatry	The art of speech-making, or the treatment of disorders of the feet
poignant	Sad looking, or penetrating and affecting
poltroon	A person of mixed race, or a craven coward
polymath	A systematic mathematician, or a person versed in many areas of learning
potable	Suitable for drinking, or easily carried
preciosity	Excessive refinement of speech, or effeminate mannerisms
predicate	To assert as a fact, or to firmly predict
predilection	A vague dislike, or a special liking
prehensile	In a primitive state, or capable of grasping
prescient	Having foresight, or easily irritated
prevaricate	To evade and mislead, or to argue fiercely
prima facie	Unfounded allegations, or self-evident
probity	Serious and analytical, or proven integrity

proclivity	A strong and natural tendency, or rising ground in a landscape
prolapse	A recurrence of a disorder, or the downward displacement of an organ
prolix	Tediously long-winded, or the centre of an ellipse
propinquity	Warning signals, or nearness
propitious	Subject to loss of balance, or favourable
pro rata	Payment for professional duties, or in the same proportion
proscribe	To forbid, or to prescribe under duress
proselytise	To translate thoughts into words, or to convert someone from one opinion or belief to another
prosthesis	Replacement of a body part with an artificial substitute, or an unwelcome medical opinion
protean	Versatile and changeable, or of vast girth
provenance	Certificate of proof of authenticity, or place of origin
prurient	Pure in thought and deed, or inquisitive about the smutty and obscene
psychosomatic	Physical disorder caused by or influenced by the emotions, or terminal
puerile	Silly and childish, or offensively smelly
puissant	Self-mocking, or powerful
pukka	Genuine and reliable, or a show-off
pulchritude	Innocence and reverence, or physical beauty
pullulate	To vibrate and sway, or to breed rapidly

68

punctilious	Paying strict attention to details of conduct, or having an obsession with time
purlieus	The fashionable clothes of high society, or the outskirts and boundaries of a neighbourhood
pusillanimous	Meanfisted, or timid and cowardly
putative	Supposed or reputed, or emerging
putti	A soldier's leggings, or the naked cherubs in art and sculpture
Pyrrhic victory	A victory that is costly and fruitless, or a victory that has emerged from the ashes of defeat

Q

Select the correct usage.

(Meanings page 93)

quasi-
A quango is a quasi-autonomous national government organisation. The room featured a quasi-patterned wallpaper in blues and reds.

querulous
The matron was fed up with her querulous attitude. The teacher was delighted with her querulous approach to difficult problems.

quiddity
They were amused by the poor man's quiddity. The quiddity of a pun is its wit.

quidnunc
The position of desk clerk at the Grand Hotel was ideal for a quidnunc like Mr Peters. After losing so much money he felt like a quidnunc.

quietus
The assassination and its bloody aftermath were followed by the long-awaited quietus. The bell tolled its long and lonely quietus.

quixotic
His face reddened with quixotic anger. Charging at the defenders, he shot for goal in true quixotic style.

Questions! Questions!

What's that, Mummy? Dad – what's that thing called? Most children's requests for names are easily satisfied, but occasionally they catch us out. What do you answer when a child asks . . .

- What's that fringed bit of paper wrapped round the end of the cutlets?
- When you went and had your ring valued, what was that magnifying thing the jeweller wore on his eye?
- What's the place called where they keep and breed cats?
- When they cut hedges into all those funny shapes, what's it called?
- What are those holes called that separate postage stamps?
- When you go up stairs you step on the treads, but what are the upright bits that keep the treads apart called?

(*answers page 96*)

quondam	He met his quondam secretly each Saturday. The horse ran up to and nuzzled its quondam owner.
quorum	The conductor surveyed the vast quorum of singers. Satisfied a quorum was present, the chairman announced the start of the meeting.
quotidian	The neighbours were maddened by the quotidian uproar from the boarding house. He was a polished quotidian from Shakespeare to Keats.

R

Using the meanings given,
fill in the gaps.

(Answers page 94)

R _ belaisian	Extravagant and boisterous
racont _ _ r	An expert story-teller
ra _ _ ish	Flashy and disreputable
rail _ ery	Good-natured teasing
r _ ison d'être	Reason for existing
ranc _ _ r	Deep-seated hatred and resentment
r _ pport	Harmonious relationship
rappr _ chement	Restoration of friendly relations after some disagreement
rara a _ is	Someone or something very unusual
rati _ cination	Reasoning by the use of logic
r _ _ cous	Harsh-sounding
react _ _ nary	A person hostile to change or progress
re _ arbative	Repellant and forbidding
recalci _ rant	Stubborn and uncontrollable
rec _ _ t	To formally retract a belief or opinion
re _ herché	Rare, strange and exquisite
recidiv _ sm	Habitual relapse into criminal behaviour
rec _ _ dite	Obscure, profound and little-known

Roget's Thesaurus

Opinion is divided over *Roget's Thesaurus*, which, with some 100,000 words grouped under 1,000 headings, has been consulted over the past century and a half by many millions of word-stuck writers in search of suitable synonyms and apt antonyms. But how useful (**Utility: useful, of use, serviceable, usable, proficuous, good for, subservient**, etc) is *Roget's*, really? Despite some updating – the last in 1987 – it remains a sort of bluffer's guide, and with its jarring mix of the trendy and archaic, compositions cobbled together from its pages must look and sound very stilted indeed. By all means browse through *Roget's* for fun and even enlightenment, but for that elusive *mot juste* your best bet is a plain dictionary of synonyms.

recru _ esce	To break out afresh
rectit _ _ e	Moral integrity
red _ lent	Smelling of something that stirs the memory
redou _ table	Formidable and commanding respect
ref _ _ endum	A vote by the electorate to ratify or reject a particular issue
refra _ tory	Resistant and troublesome
reful _ ent	Shining brightly
ren _ ge	Break a promise or fail to fulfil an undertaking
rep _ eh _ nd	To criticise or blame
repudi _ te	To reject and disown
r _ trograde	To go backwards; deteriorate
retrou _ sé	Turned up
rhetor _ _ al	Concerned with effect rather than content
ri _ tus	A gaping open mouth

ripar _ _ n	Pertaining to river banks
ri _ oste	A quick and clever reply
risib _ e	Inclined to laughter
ro _ o _ o	Highly elaborate and florid 18th-century French style of decoration
r _ ué	A dissipated lecher
rum _ ustious	Boisterous and unruly

Sozzled, sloshed and squiffy

After what must have been a marinated marathon, the American wordsmith Paul Dickson came up with 2,231 words, phrases and slang expressions for intoxication. Here are just a few of them:

aced	aglow	banjanxed
besotted	bibulous	blasted
blimped	blitzed	blotto
bombed	bunnied	cockeyed
corked	crapulous	ebriose
flummoxed	embalmed	floored
gaga	fogmatic	frazzled
lathered	gone	half-sprung
non compos	lushed	motherless
overloaded	obfuscated	out to lunch
sauced	plastered	roostered
totalled	schnoggered	shellacked
zippered	umbriago	varnished

S

Which of the two meanings is correct?

(Answers page 94)

salacious	Obscene and lustful, or obsessively jealous
salient	Highly conspicuous, or with a following wind
salutary	Formal, or beneficial
sang-froid	Haughty manner, or coolness and composure under pressure
sardonic	Sneering and scornful, or shy and retiring
Sassenach	An English person, or a Scot
saturnine	Having a mane of black hair, or melancholic
savoir-faire	Extremely witty, or having a fine sense of what's right and wrong socially
scaramouch	A boastful buffoon, or a young beggar
scatology	Having a great knowledge of trivia, or an unhealthy interest in excrement
Schadenfreude	Delight in another's misfortunes, or to remain calm in a heated argument
scintilla	A group of bright stars, or the tiniest, most minute particle
scrivener	A clerk who writes up documents, or an official who supervises patients' debts to hospitals
scut	A rabbit's tail, or a short levering tool
sebaceous	Prone to skin complaints, or fatty

75

secular	Pertaining to sacred things, or pertaining to worldly things
sedulous	Persistent and diligent, or casual
semantics	Concerned with the sounds of words, or concerned with the meanings of words
semiotics	The study of signs in communications, or the study of Indian languages
senescent	Becoming young again, or growing old
sententious	Self-deceiving, or pompous moralising
sequestered	Cut out of an inheritance, or secluded
serendipitous	The inclination to find things unexpectedly, or the ability to make others happy
serrated	Saw-toothed, or rough like sandpaper
shibboleth	A password, gesture or mark that distinguishes a group of people, or a perpetuated untruth
sibilant	A silently sounded letter in a word, or the sound of a hiss
silviculture	Silkworm farming, or forestry
similitude	Resemblance, or the feeling of weightlessness
simony	False accusation, or trading in sacred objects
simulacrum	A shadowy, deceptive likeness, or a recurring nightmare
sinecure	A well-paid cushy position, or the inability to bend an arm at the elbow
sinistral	A hot wind that blows from the Mediterranean, or left-handed
skulk	To lurk unseen with wrongdoing in mind, or to run away from trouble
sobriquet	Flowers presented to a singer after a performance, or a nickname
sodality	Malicious scheming, or companionship
soi-disant	Devil-may-care, or 'self-styled'
soigné	Elaborately well-groomed, or a jewelled clasp for the hair

soirée	An evening of conversation and music, or a gathering of female friends
solecism	A recorded sun-spot, or a grammatical mistake
solipsism	The theory that only the self is real and knowable, or an unforgivable social gaffe
sommelier	A brandy warehouse, or a wine waiter
somnambulism	Talking to the spirit world, or sleepwalking
sonorous	Giving out a full, rich sound, or a person with a knowledge of the Mexican language
sophistry	The use of fallacious and deceptive argument, or having a preference for one's own sex
soporific	Oily, or sleep-inducing
sotto voce	Slightly inebriated, or in an undertone
spavined	Worn out and broken down, or split in two
specious	Seemingly right and correct but actually not, or undersized
splenetic	Tendency to be constantly ill, or bad-tempered
sporadic	At regular intervals, or occurring occasionally
stasis	A static state, or an irregular heartbeat
stentorian	A strict teacher, or loud and powerful
stultify	To make something appear foolish and absurd, or to check growth
stygian	Bottomless depths, or impenetrably dark
subliminal	Something perceived below the threshhold of consciousness, or thought transference
subsume	To include or absorb into, or to reduce
succinct	Easily dissolved, or sharp and concise
supercilious	Grossly superficial, or arrogantly indifferent

supernumerary	Superfluous, or every hundredth person or object in a group
suppurate	To vibrate, or to fester
surrogate	An appointed substitute, or a person dependent upon public funds
svelte	Slim and graceful, or superbly groomed
sybaritic	A worshipper of Satan, or indulging in sensual pleasures
sycophantic	Servile flattery, or complaining about details
symbiosis	Mutually advantageous partnership of two dissimilar organisms, or the ability of some fluids to permeate through others without being absorbed
synergy	Artificially induced energy, or co-operative activity to produce enhanced benefits
syntax	The rules of grammar that arrange the words in a sentence, or the accents in speech

T

Choose the correct meaning.

(Answers page 94)

tachometer	measures distance; forward speed; speed of rotation
tacit	surly; implied; obvious
tactile	pertaining to sense of sight; pertaining to sense of touch; pertaining to sense of hearing
talisman	a charm; a potion; a blood-bond
tangible	chewy; ethereal; real
taupe	pale purple; grey-brown; silvery
telekinesis	ability to hear unearthly voices; ability to spin the head around; ability to move things without touching them
temerity	boldness; meekness; harshness
temporal	spiritual; official; earthly
temporise	to delay; to half-finish something; to gloat
tendentious	boring; biased; cautious
tenet	a sharp lesson; a belief; a criticism
tenuous	flimsy; extremely long; complicated
tercentenary	an anniversary of 200 years; an anniversary of 300 years; an anniversary of 400 years
tessellated	chequered; fringed; stepped

theism	belief in rule by religion; belief in one God; belief in existence of many gods
thrall	excitement; bondage; fear
timorous	fearful; tiny; loud-voiced
tinnitus	disease of the skin; inflammation of the knee joint; ringing in the ears
tocsin	an alarm; a virulent poison; an antidote
torpid	sluggish; warm; slithery
tort	a junior judge; a private or civil wrong; a criminal offence
tractable	easily traced; easily swallowed; docile
traduce	to defame; to seduce; to persuade
tranche	to simmer; to multiply; a portion
transcend	to rise beyond; to disappear; to go across
transient	speedy; fleeting; a lover of travel
travail	painful toil; uncomfortable travelling; wailing at a funeral

80

tremulous	lisping; singing in low register; trembling
trenchant	cutting and forceful; eating with gusto; living underground
trichology	study of shells; study of combustible matter; study of hair
tridactyl	having a long tail; having three fingers or toes; having armoured scales
triptych	a painting on three panels; a religious sculpture; a three-handled vase
triumvirate	a gathering of cardinals; a group of three people wielding power; a three-cornered hat
troglodyte	a gargoyle; a large toad; a cave dweller
trompe l'oeil	lavender bath oil; a painting that gives the illusion of reality; a resounding victory
trope	a figure of speech; a malarial infection; a woman's pith helmet
truncate	to cut off the top; to cut off the bottom; to cut off the sides
tumescent	decaying; dozing; becoming swollen
turbid	cloudy; distended; sexually aroused
turpitude	inherent depravity; moral uprightness; strength of character
tyro	a seducer; a good-for-nothing; a beginner

U

Select the correct usage.

(Meanings page 95)

ubiquitous
In summer the ubiquitous dandelions dazzle the eye. The ubiquitous landlord extracted ferocious rents from his tenants.

ullage
The shipowner was fined for tipping ullage into the river. The wine merchant complained about the excessive ullage in the barrels.

ululate
He watched as the dancer ululated her body. As darkness approached he waited for the wolves to ululate.

umbrage
She took umbrage at the slightest criticism. The cellar was damp and reeked of umbrage.

unconscionable
He took an unconscionable time to walk to the rostrum. On several occasions during the day she would lapse into unconscionable dreams.

unctuous
After the sermon everyone felt decidedly unctuous. He addressed them in unctuous tones.

unilateral
The convoy steered a unilateral course. The governor made a unilateral decision to suspend the constitution.

Usage

Roughly speaking, there is **Correct English** and there is **Usage**. Usage is what the majority of people do with the language, and it is often at odds with what is considered to be correct. It sometimes happens that people will begin to use a word wrongly, and soon almost everyone is doing the same. When this happens, some linguists say that the wrong usage then becomes the right usage. If, for example, most people say and believe that the **hoi polloi** are the toffs (it actually means the common people) then that becomes the accepted meaning. If people believe that **lemmings** are little rodents that follow each other into the sea in large numbers and drown (which they do only exceedingly rarely) then that is the correct definition. **Aggravate** is another case. It means to worsen, but many people think it means to annoy (confirmed by research polls), and this belief is growing. So in your lifetime you may witness one of the wonders of English: a word that, through incorrect usage by ordinary speakers, changes its meaning.

urbane	She arrived with her rich, urbane escort. He looked utterly urbane in his string vest and seedy jacket.
usurious	The upheaval left them anxious and usurious. He had no alternative but to borrow the money at usurious rates.
uxorious	Fred's wages were completely at the mercy of his uxorious nature. She loved the room, with its faintly uxorious atmosphere.

V

Using the meanings given,
fill in the gaps.

(Answers page 95)

vaci _ _ ate	To waver, or sway this way and that
valetu _ inarian	A chronic invalid
vapi _	Insipid, dull and flat
v _ nal	Unprincipled and ready to accept a bribe
vende _ _ a	A long-lasting blood-feud
ve _ acity	Honesty and truthfulness
verba _ im	Word for word
verisim _ litude	Appearance of being true
ver _ acular	The native language, habits or activities of a locality
ve _ nal	Pertaining to spring
vertig _ nous	Whirling round at a dizzy rate
vic _ _ ious	Experienced or imagined through the words or deeds of another
vicen _ ial	Every twenty years
vici _ _ itude	A change or variation
v _ lify	To defame
vir _ u	A taste for the rare, curious and beautiful
vis- _ -vis	In relation to
vis _ eral	Arising from the viscera, or from deep feeling
vitia _ e	To corrupt or spoil

v _ treous	Of glass or glasslike
vi _ uperation	Abuse in harsh language
volit _ on	Free exercise of the will
volte-f _ ce	Reversal of point of view or attitude
v _ luptuary	A person devoted to self-indulgence and luxury
vouch _ afe	To grant with condescension

Vowels

As languages go, English is not over-endowed with vowels; one Vietnamese language has 55. On the other hand, some 80,000 Abkhazo speakers in the Caucasus Mountains manage with only two. In the English language it is not unusual to find words containing all five vowels, but finding words with vowels only is rather more difficult. One of them is **euouae**, a term used in Gregorian music; another is **aiaiai**, the roseate spoonbill. And, cheating a bit, there is the ancient Tuscan city of **Oueioi**, and Circe's fabled island of **Aeaea**.

W

Which of the two meanings
is correct?

(Answers page 95)

wagon-lit	A coach lamp, or a sleeping car on a continental train
wizened	Dried and shrivelled, or very learned
wraith	A ghostly apparition of a living person or someone who has just died, or a phosphorescent mist rising from swamp water
wrangler	One with first class mathematical honours at Cambridge University, or same at Oxford University
wunderkind	The doctrines of the Lutheran Church, or a child prodigy

---

Webster's 'dirty' dictionary

When *Webster's Third International Dictionary* was published in 1961 it caused a storm by listing such no-no's as **ain't** [Contraction of am not: 'I'm going too, ain't I?'] and **piss-poor** – which brought upon Webster's the ire of a bishop, who wrote, 'The greatest of all American dictionaries has been corrupted at the center.'

X, Y and Z

Which of the two meanings is correct?

(*Answers page 95*)

xanthic   Ability to survive with little moisture or water, or yellowish

yahoo   Brutish half-human creature, or a type of monkey found in Madagascar

yashmak   Cheese made from yak's milk, or the veil worn by Muslim women in public

zealot   A fantatic, or an ornamental brass tray

zeitgeist   The spirit of an age, or the collective spirits of the dead

zenith   The lowest point, or the highest point

ziggurat   A terraced, pyramidal temple, or an experimental airship of the 1930s

zwieback   A wild boar, or a type of sweet cake

Answers

Where words were followed by two or three possible definitions, the definitions are identified here in order by the letters a, b and c. For example, the first word below is **abstruse**; of the three definitions, the correct one is the second one, 'hard to understand', which is identified as **b**.

A abstruse, b; accretion, a; Achilles' heel, c; acolyte, a; acrimony, b; actuary, b; acumen, b; affidavit, a; *aficionado*, b; agnostic, c; agronomy, c; akimbo, a; alfresco, c; *alter ego*, a; amalgam, a; amanuensis, b; ambidextrous, c; ambivalent, b; amortise, a; anachronism, c; analogous, c; anathema, a; *angst*, c; annul, a; animus, a; anosmia, c; antipathy, b; antonym, b; aperient, b; aphorism, c; apiarian, c; aplomb, a; apocalyptic, a; apogee, c; apposite, c; apostasy, b; appurtenance, a; aquiline, c; arachnid, c; arbitrage, a; arcane, b; argot, c; Armageddon, b; armoire, c; arraign, a; *arriviste*, a; asinine, c; assuage, b; atrophy, a; attenuate, c; attrition, b; *au fait*, b; avuncular, a

B *badinage*; bacchanalian; Bakelite; baleful; balustrade; bardolatry; bar mitzvah; baroque; bathos; bayou; beatitude; behemoth; *bel canto*; bellicose; bellwether; bemused; benign; besmirch; *bête noire*; bibelot; biennial; bifurcate; *bijou*; bilateral; binary; biopsy; blasé; blench; blithely; bona fide; *bonhomie*; bon vivant; boreal; bothy; bourgeoisie; bowdlerise; braggadocio; braise; Brobdignagian; *brouhaha*; brusque; bucolic; bulimia; bumptious; burgeoning; burlap; burnish; busboy; Byronic

C cabal, a; cabriole, a; cache, b; cajole, a; calcareous, a;
callipygian, b; callisthenics, a; calumny, a; camaraderie, b;
campanology, b; canard, a; candour, a; cantankerous, a;
captious, b; carcanet, b; carpal, a; *carte blanche*, b; cartel, a;
castellated, b; castigate, a; catalysis, a; catamite, a;
catharsis, b; catheter, a; *causerie*, a; *caveat emptor*, b; cavil, a;
celerity, a; chancel, b; charlatan, a; chauvinism, a;
chiaroscuro, b; chicanery, b; chiffonier, a; chimera, a;
choleric, b; chutzpah, b; cinéaste, a; *circa*, a;
circumlocution, b; circumscribed, b; clandestine, b;
clement, a; *cognoscenti*, a; colloquy, b; collude, b; comity, a;
complaisant, b; concomitant, b; concupiscence, a;
conflation, a; consanguinity, b; contemn, b; contretemps, a;
corpus delicti, a; coruscate, b; costive, b; coterie, a;
crapulous, b; crescendo, b; cruciform, a; crustaceans, b;
cultivar, a; cupidity, b; cynosure, a; cytology, b

D dado, b; dalliance, a; dearth, b; débâcle, c; debilitate, c;
déclassé, a; declivity, b; *de facto*, a; defalcate, b;
defenestration, c; *dégagé*, a; *déjà vu*, c; deleterious, a;
delphic, c; demagoguery, b; *demi-monde*, b; demotic, a;
demurrer, a; dénouement, c; depilatory, b; *de rigueur*, a;
desiccate, b; desultory, b; determinism, c; dextral, b;
dialectic, b; dichotomy, c; didactic, a; dilatory, a;
dipsomaniac, c; discommode, b; discrete, a; disparage, c;
dissemble, a; distrain, a; diurnal, a; divertissement, c;
doctrinaire, a; dolorous, c; double entendre, b; doughty, a;
doyen, c; draconian, b; drugget, a; dudgeon, b;
duodenum, c

E ebullient; effulgent; egalitarian; egocentric; egregious; *élan*; elegiac; elephantine; élite; Elysian; emanate; emancipate; emasculate; embargo; embolism; embryonic; emendate; emollient; emolument; empathy; empirical; encomium; endemic; enervate; *enfant terrible*; engender; enigma; enjoin; ennui; enormity; enunciate; ephemera; epicure; epigram; equitable; equivocal; ergonomics; erogenous; ersatz; eructation; erudite; esoteric; *esprit de corps*; ethos; etymology; eugenics; eulogise; euphemism; euphoria; Eurasian; euthanasia; evanescent; exacerbate; excoriate; exculpate; execrable; exegesis; exemplary; exorcise; expatiate; expatriate; expiate; expropriate; expurgate; extirpate

F facile, a; factotum, a; *fait accompli*, a; fallacy, b; farrago, b; fascism, a; fastidious, b; fatuous, a; *faux pas*, b; fealty, b; febrile, b; feckless, a; fecund, a; felicitous, a; feral, b; fervid, b; filibuster, b; flaccid, a; flews, b; flippant, a; florescence, a; florid, a; flout, b; foible, b; forensic, a; fortuitous, b; fractious, a; friable, b; fulgent, a; fulminate, a; fulsome, b; fundamentalism, a; furbelow, a; furlough, b

G gaffe [b] = tactless remark or blunder; gambit [a] = an opening move; gamut [a] = a whole range; garrulous [b] = talkative; gauche [b] = awkward and socially graceless; gazebo [a] = a small summerhouse with a view; gefilte fish [a] = fish meal and eggs, shaped into balls and poached; genuflect [a] = to bend the knee; germane [b] = relevant; gerrymander [a] = manipulation of electoral boundaries to give a candidate an unfair advantage; gestation [b] = the period from conception to birth; *gesundheit* [a] = 'Good Health!'; gigolo [b] = a paid male escort, or kept man; glutinous [a] = sticky; gobbet [a] = a lump or piece; gobbledegook [b] = pompous jargon; gourmandise [b] = to eat excessively; grandiose [a] = impressive, perhaps pretentiously so; gratuitous [b] = uncalled for; gravamen [a] = the key point or gist of a legal action; gregarious [a] = one who enjoys company; gumption [b] = energetic initiative

H habeas corpus, b; *habitué*, a; hackneyed, b;
hagiography, c; ha-ha, a; halcyon, a; halitosis, c; hapless, c;
harbinger, a; hector, c; hegemony, b; heinous, b;
hellebore, b; heresy, a; heterogeneous, b; heuristic, a;
hiatus, a; Hibernian, b; hindsight, c; histology, a;
hogmanay, a; *hoi polloi*, b; hologram, c; homogeneous, a;
honorarium, b; hortatory, c; hubris, a; humanism, b;
humdrum, b; hydrology, a; hygrometer, a; hyperbole, a

I iconoclast; idiomatic; idiosyncrasy; idolatry; ignominy;
imbroglio; immolate; immured; immutable; impasse;
implacable; importune; imprimatur; impromptu; impugn;
inadvertent; incipient; incognito; inculcate; incumbent;
indemnity; indigenous; indigent; ineffable; ineluctable;
inexorable; *infra dig*; *ingénue*; ingenuous; inimical; innate;
innocuous; innuendo; insalubrious; insidious; insouciant;
inter alia; interdict; internecine; interstice; intransigent;
intrinsic; introvert; inveigh; invidious; irascible; irrevocable

J jaundiced, a; jejune, b; jeopardy, a; jeremiad, b;
jettison, a; jihad, a; jingoism, b; jocose, a; *joie de vivre*, a;
junta, a; juvenescence, b; juxtapose, a

K karma [b] = destiny; kibbutz [a] = an Israeli community
farm; kitsch [a] = sentimental, garish or pretentious (usually
art); kleptomaniac [a] = obsessive thief; kosher [b] = food
prepared in accordance with Jewish dietary laws; kowtow [b]
= to behave in a servile way; kudos [b] = praise and credit

L lachrymose, b; laconic, a; lacuna, a; laity, b; *laissez-faire*, c; lambent, b; lampoon, b; languor, a; largess, c; lascivious, a; latent, a; lateral, c; laudable, b; legerdemain, b; leitmotif, a; *lèse-majesté*, c; lethargic, b; libido, b; libretto, a; licentious, a; lickerish, c; lionize, b; lissom, c; locum tenens, a; logorrhea, b; *longueur*, c; loquacious, a; Lothario, a; *louche*, c; lubricious, c; lugubrious, a; lumpen, b

M macerate, b; Machiavellian, a; macrocosm, a; magisterial, a; *magnum opus*, b; maladroit, a; malaise, b; malapropism, b; *mal de mer*, b; malfeasance, b; Malthusian, a; maudlin, a; maunder, b; *mea culpa*, b; megalomania, b; megrim, a; *mélange*, a; mêlée, b; mellifluous, b; ménage, a; mendacious, a; mendicant, b; mephitic, a; meretricious, b; mesmerise, a; metabolism, a; *métier*, a; metronymic, b; micron, b; micturate, b; milieu, a; millennium, a; minatory, a; misanthropy, b; miscegenation, b; misnomer, a; misogyny, a; mnemonic, b; moiety, a; moire, b; monograph, b; moratorium, a; moribund, a; *mot juste*, b; mufti, b; mundane, a; myocardiogram, b; myopia, b

N nadir; nascent; nebulous; necropsy; nefarious; negus; nemesis; neologism; neophyte; nephritis; nepotism; nexus; nihilism; noisome; nonage; nonchalant; *non sequitur*; nostrum; nubile; nugatory

O obdurate, b; obeisance, a; obfuscate, c; obloquy, c; obsequious, b; obsolescent, a; obstreperous, a; obviate, c; occidental, b; occlude, b; odium, a; odontologist, c; oenologist, b; *oeuvre*, c; oligarchy, b; omniscient, a; opprobrium, a; oracular, b; orotund, c; ossified, b; ostensibly, a; ostentatious, b; osteopathy, c; otiose, a; *outré*, c; overt, b

P paediatrician, b; palaver, a; palpable, a; panacea, a; panache, a; Panglossian, a; panegyric, b; panjandrum, b; pantheism, a; paparazzi, b; paradigm, a; paragon, b; parameter, b; paramour, b; paranoia, b; paraphrase, a; pariah, b; *pari mutuel*, b; parlous, b; parsimony, b; parvenu, a; *passé*, b; pastiche, a; paterfamilias, a; pathogenic, b; patina, b; patisserie, a; patrial, a; patrician, b; Pecksniffian, b; pectorals, a; pedagogue, b; pedantry, a; peignoir, b; pejorative, a; pellucid, a; percipient, b; peregrination, a; peremptory, b; perennial, b; perfunctory, a; peripatetic, b; periphrasis, a; pernicious, b; peroration, b; perquisite, a; persiflage, a; perspicacious, b; pertinacious, b; philanderer, a; philistine, a; phlegmatic, b; physiognomy, b; picayune, a; *pied-à-terre*, a; pinnate, b; pixilated, a; placebo, a; plagiarism, b; plangent, a; Platonic, b; plebeian, b; plenary, a; plethora, a; plutocracy, a; podiatry, b; poignant, b; poltroon, b; polymath, b; potable, a; preciosity, a; predicate, a; predilection, b; prehensile, b; prescient, a; prevaricate, a; prima facie, b; probity, b; proclivity, a; prolapse, b; prolix, a; propinquity, b; propitious, b; pro rata, b; proscribe, a; proselytise, b; prosthesis, a; protean, a; provenance, b; prurient, b; psychosomatic, a; puerile, a; puissant, b; pukka, a; pulchritude, b; pullulate, b; punctilious, a; purlieus, b; pusillanimous, b; putative, a; putti, b; Pyrric victory, a

Q quasi [a] = having the semblance of, not quite, querulous [a] = of a complaining disposition; quiddity [b] = the essence or uniqueness of something; quidnunc [a] = a gossip; quietus [a] = final conclusion; quixotic [b] = possessing high but impractical aims; quondam [b] = former; quorum [b] = an agreed number of people required to be present before a meeting can be held; quotidian [a] = occurring daily

R Rabelaisian; raconteur; raffish; raillery; *raison d'être*; rancour; rapport; *rapprochement*; *rara avis*; ratiocination; raucous; reactionary; rebarbative; recalcitrant; recant; recherché; recidivism; recondite; recrudesce; rectitude; redolent; redoubtable; referendum; refractory; refulgent; renege; reprehend; repudiate; retrograde; *retroussé*; rhetorical; rictus; riparian; riposte; risible; rococo; roué; rumbustious

S salacious, a; salient, a; salutary, b; sang-froid, b; sardonic, a; Sassenach, a; saturnine, b; *savoir-faire*, b; scaramouch, a; scatology, b; *Schadenfreude*, a; scintilla, b; scrivener, a; scut, a; sebaceous, b; secular, b; sedulous, a; semantics, b; semiotics, a; senescent, b; sententious, b; sequestered, b; serendipitous, a; serrated, a; shibboleth, a; sibilant, b; silviculture, b; similitude, a; simony, b; simulacrum, a; sinecure, a; sinistral, b; skulk, a; sobriquet, b; sodality, b; soi-disant, b; *soigné*, a; soirée, a; solecism, b; solipsism, a; sommelier, b; somnambulism, b; sonorous, a; sophistry, a; soporific, b; *sotto voce*, b; spavined, a; specious, a; splenetic, b; sporadic, b; stasis, a; stentorian, b; stultify, a; stygian, b; subliminal, a; subsume, a; succinct, b; supercilious, b; supernumerary, a; suppurate, b; surrogate, a; svelte, a; sybaritic, b; sycophantic, a; symbiosis, a; synergy, b; syntax, a

T tachometer, c; tacit, b; tactile, b; talisman, a; tangible, c; taupe, b; telekinesis, c; temerity, a; temporal, c; temporise, a; tendentious, b; tenet, b; tenuous, a; tercentenary, b; tessellated, a; theism, b; thrall, b; timorous, a; tinnitus, c; tocsin, a; torpid, a; tort, b; tractable, c; traduce, a; tranche, c; transcend, a; transient, b; travail, a; tremulous, c; trenchant, a; trichology, c; tridactyl, b; triptych, a; triumvirate, b; troglodyte, c; *trompe l'oeil*, b; trope, a; truncate, a; tumescent, c; turbid, a; turpitude, a; tyro, c

U ubiquitous [a] = existing everywhere; ullage [b] = the space in a container not taken up by its contents; ullulate [b] = to howl or wail; umbrage [a] = a sense of slight or injury; unconscionable [a] = going beyond reasonable bounds; unctuous [b] = excessively suave and moralising; unilateral [b] = something done or undertaken by a single person or party; urbane [a] = polite and polished; usurious [b] = extortionate interest on loans; uxorious [a] = excessive doting on a wife

V vacillate; valetudinarian; vapid; venal; vendetta; veracity; verbatim; verisimilitude; vernacular; vernal; vertiginous; vicarious; vicennial; vicissitude; vilify; virtu; vis-a-vis; visceral; vitiate; vitreous; vituperation; volition; volte-face; voluptuary; vouchsafe

W wagon-lit, b; wizened, a; wraith, a; wrangler, a; wunderkind, b

X, Y and Z xanthic, b; yahoo, a; yashmak, b; zealot, a; zeitgeist, a; zenith, b; ziggurat, a; zwieback, b

Word playtime The four words each contain all five vowels. The four-letter word common to all the sports listed is *hook*.

Know what I mean? 1. cornice 2. clutch pedal
3. Braille 4. groynes 5. davenport 6. phrenology
7. Clydesdale 8. zodiac 9. karaoke 10. tic-tac men

The nous on dous hazardous, horrendous, stupendous and tremendous

Questions! Questions! 1. papillote 2. loupe
3. cattery 4. topiary 5. perforations 6. risers

Two or more of a kind 1. A *pack* of hounds 2. A *murder* of crows 3. A *covey* of partridges 4. A *business* of ferrets 5. A *dray* of squirrels 6. A *pride/troop* of lions
7. An *exaltation* of larks 8. A *chattering* of starlings
9. A *herd* of whales 10. A *mustering* of storks